Humankind

Level B

Edited by Helen Webber and Marianne Carus

Open Court Publishing Company
La Salle, Illinois 61301

Acknowledgments For permission to reprint copyrighted material, grateful acknowledgment is made to the following publishers, authors, and agents:

Constance Whitman Baher for "Now You See It, Now You Don't" from *Cricket* Magazine, September 1974, copyright © 1974 by Constance Whitman Baher. Illustration copyright © Open Court Publishing Company 1974.

Coward, McCann & Geoghegan, Inc., for "The Bunk Bed" from *Gus and Buster Work Things Out* by Andrew Bronin, copyright © 1975 by Andrew Bronin. Illustrations copyright © Open Court Publishing Company 1975.

Cricket Magazine, September 1974, for "Riddles," illustrations by Quentin Blake. Copyright © Open Court Publishing Company 1974.

Thomas Y. Crowell Company, Inc., for "Make a Fossil" from *Fossils Tell Of Long Ago* by Aliki Brandenberg, copyright © 1972 by Aliki Brandenberg.

Dennis Dobson Publishers for "My Sister Laura" from *Silly Verse For Kids* by Spike Milligan. Illustration copyright © Open Court Publishing Company 1974.

Farrar, Straus & Giroux, Inc., and Valerie Worth Bahlke for "Clock" from *Small Poems* by Valerie Worth, copyright © 1972 by Valerie Worth. Illustration copyright © Open Court Publishing Company 1976.

Aileen Fisher for "Mouse Dinner" from *Cricket* Magazine, June 1975, copyright © 1975 by Aileen Fisher. Illustration copyright © Open Court Publishing Company 1975.

Greenwillow Books and Curtis Brown, Ltd., for "Serendipity" from *Mr. Brimble's Hobby and Other Stories* by Eve Rice, copyright © 1975 by Eve Rice.

Karen Gundersheimer for "Apples" from *Cricket* Magazine, September 1974, copyright © 1974 by Karen Gundersheimer. Illustrations copyright © Open Court Publishing Company 1974.

Harper & Row, Publishers, Inc., for "No More Woxes" from *I'll Be You and You Be Me* by Ruth Krauss, illustrated by Maurice Sendak, text copyright © 1954 by Ruth Krauss, pictures copyright © 1954 by Maurice Sendak.

Harper & Row, Publishers, Inc., and Ruth Krauss for "How to Be Inside a Whale" and "How to Draw with Your Toes" from *How To Make An Earthquake* by Ruth Krauss, text copyright © 1954 by Ruth Krauss. Illustrations copyright© Open Court Publishing Company 1975.

Harper & Row, Publishers, Inc., and World's Work, Ltd., for "A Swim" from *Frog and Toad Are Friends,* text and illustrations by Arnold Lobel, copyright © 1970 by Arnold Lobel.

Holt, Rinehart and Winston, Publishers, and Curtis Brown, Ltd., for "Everett Anderson's Year" from *Everett Anderson's Year* by Lucille Clifton, illustrated by Ann Grifalconi, copyright © 1974 by Lucille Clifton, copyright © 1974 by Ann Grifalconi.

Joan Resnikoff for "The Diver" by Alexander Resnikoff from *Cricket* Magazine, May 1974, copyright © 1974 by Alexander Resnikoff. Illustrations copyright © Open Court Publishing Company 1974.

Russell & Volkening, Inc., as agents for the author for "A Story in Pictures" by Sheila Greenwald from *Cricket* Magazine, March 1974, copyright © 1974 by Sheila Greenwald; and for "Meg's Egg" by Mary Ann Hoberman from *Cricket* Magazine, November 1975, copyright © 1975 by Mary Ann Hoberman. Illustration copyright © Open Court Publishing Company 1975.

Printed in the United States
5099607601
ISBN 0-87548-710-6

Contents

A SWIM

Arnold Lobel

Toad and Frog

went down to the river.

"What a day for a swim," said Frog.

"Yes," said Toad.

"I will go behind these rocks

and put on my bathing suit."

"I don't wear a bathing suit,"

said Frog.

"Well, I do," said Toad.

Illustrations by the author

"After I put on my bathing suit,
you must not look at me
until I get into the water."

"Why not?"

asked Frog.

"Because I look funny

in my bathing suit.

That is why," said Toad.

Frog closed his eyes when Toad

came out from behind the rocks.

Toad was wearing his bathing suit.

"Don't peek," he said.

Frog and Toad jumped

into the water.

They swam all afternoon.

Frog swam fast

and made big splashes.

Toad swam slowly

and made smaller splashes.

A turtle came along the riverbank.

"Frog, tell that turtle

to go away," said Toad.

"I do not want him to see me

in my bathing suit

when I come out of the river."

Frog swam over to the turtle.

"Turtle," said Frog,

"you will have to go away."

"Why should I?" asked the turtle.

"Because Toad thinks that

he looks funny in his bathing suit,

and he does not want you to see him,"

said Frog.

Some lizards were sitting nearby.

"Does Toad really look funny

in his bathing suit?" they asked.

A snake crawled out of the grass.

"If Toad looks funny

in his bathing suit," said the snake,

"then I, for one, want to see him."

"We want to see him too,"
said two dragonflies.

"Me too," said a field mouse.

"I have not seen anything funny

in a long time."

Frog swam back to Toad.

"I am sorry, Toad," he said. "Everyone

wants to see how you will look."

"Then I will stay right here

until they go away," said Toad.

The turtle and the lizards

and the snake and the dragonflies

and the field mouse

all sat on the riverbank.

They waited for Toad to come

out of the water.

"Please," cried Frog, "please go away!"

But no one went away.

Toad was getting colder and colder.

He was beginning to shiver and sneeze.

"I will have to come out of the water,"

said Toad. "I am catching a cold."

Toad climbed

out of the river.

The water dripped

out of his bathing suit

and down onto his feet.

The turtle laughed.

The lizards laughed.

The snake laughed.

The field mouse laughed,

and Frog laughed.

"What are you laughing at, Frog?"
said Toad.

"I am laughing at you, Toad,"
said Frog,

"because you *do* look funny

in your bathing suit."

"Of course I do," said Toad.

Then he picked up his clothes

and went home.

THE DIVER

Alexander Resnikoff

This time I'll do it! Mommy, look!
I promise I won't be a fool—
I'm going to climb on that diving board
And dive right into the pool!

Look at me, Mom; I'm doing it!
I never have done it before—
I'm climbing those steps to the diving board.
I'll count them: One, two, three, four. . . .

Look, Mom! I'm on the diving board!
This carpet feels terribly rough—
It hurts the tan on the soles of my feet,
But I can take it; I'm tough.

And now I'm jumping up and down
Right by the steps—Mommy, look!
You sure you're looking? Saw me jump?
Now *please*, Mommy, put down that book!

Illustrations by Karen Gundersheimer

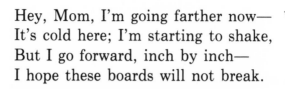

Hey, Mom, I'm going farther now—
It's cold here; I'm starting to shake,
But I go forward, inch by inch—
I hope these boards will not break.

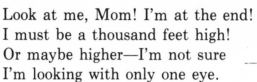

Look at me, Mom! I'm at the end!
I must be a thousand feet high!
Or maybe higher—I'm not sure
I'm looking with only one eye.

I'll say a prayer, I'll take a deep breath,
I'll hold my nose, and I'll plop—
Maybe you should move a little way back—
Those waves might go over the top!

Mom, are you looking? Watch me now!
I hope that you are prepared—
Look at me, Mommy, here I come—
One. . .
Two. . .
Three. . .
. . . .
. . . .
I am scared. . . .

How to Be Ruth Inside a Whale Krauss

First, you get in bed and you crawl under the covers and pull them over your head. If it's not dark enough, you should close your eyes, too. Now you're inside the whale. Other things are in there with you, little fishes and some pearls and maybe some seaweed. If you want to look out, you can look through little holes. And when you want to get out again, you ask the whale politely and it lets you out.

If you want to just take a swim, you can go out and then come back in.

Illustration by Crockett Johnson

How to Draw with Your Toes

Ruth Krauss

Sit on the floor and put the pencil between your toes. You have to do this with your other foot. No using hands. And be sure the pencil is point-side down, because if it isn't, you'll have to lie on your stomach, and then you can't see very well what you're drawing. You mustn't hold the paper with your hands either. If you feel too much like using them, you should do something else with them.

Sometimes toe drawings are very light. They could even be too light to see. You have to practice. If you practice enough, you could draw with both feet at once. And if you can wiggle your ears too, you could be in the circus.

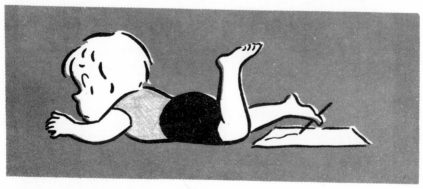

Illustration by Crockett Johnson

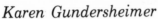

Karen Gundersheimer

Apples in the treetops,
Apples on the ground.
Apples in the kitchen,
Apples all around.

Shiny red and golden yellow—
Eat them *all*, you greedy fellow!
Polish them and juggle them, toss them in the air,
Apples in the autumn, apples everywhere.

Apples in the basket,
Apples from the tree—
Apples for the neighbors,
Apples for you and me.

Illustrations by the author

A Story in Pictures

Sheila Greenwald

4

5

6

7

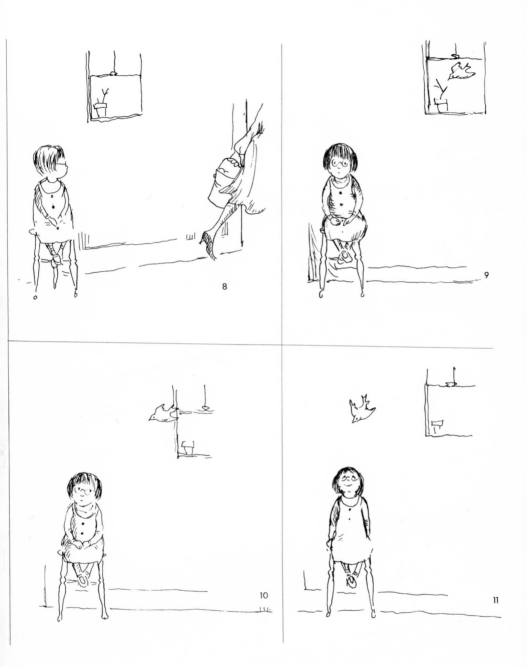

12

13

14

15

22

16

17

18

19

20

21

22

23

24

25

26

27

28

29

30

31

No More Woxes

A Short Tall Tale by Ruth Krauss

There was a wolf
and there was a fox and
they ate each other up.
And that made the wox.

Then the wox
ate himself up and
that's why there are
no more woxes.

27

Illustrations by Maurice Sendak

Make a Fossil

Aliki

How would you like to make a fossil?
Not a one-million-year-old fossil but a
　　one-minute-old "fossil."
Make a clay imprint of your hand, like this:

Take some clay.
Flatten it out.
Press your hand in the clay.
Lift your hand away.

Your hand is gone, but its shape is in the clay.
You made an imprint.
The imprint shows what your hand is like, the way
　　a dinosaur's track shows us what his foot was like.

Suppose, when it dried, you buried your clay imprint.
Suppose, a million years from now, someone found it.
Your imprint would be hard as stone.

28

Illustrations by the author

It would be a fossil of your hand.
It would tell something about you.
It would tell the finder something about life on earth
a million years earlier.

Every time anyone finds a fossil we learn more about
life on earth long ago.
Someday you may find a fossil, one that is millions
and millions of years old.
You may discover something that no one knows today.

RIDDLES

What did the frog say when he was in inch-high water?
"Kneedeep!"

Paul Turpin, age 6
Federal Way, Washington

What is a pigskin used for most often?
To hold a pig together.

Susan Foote, age 9
Terryville, Connecticut

When the prisoner was freed from jail, he said, "I'm free! I'm free!" What did the little boy say?

"So what, I'm four."

Patty Schultz, age 9
Weyanwega, Wisconsin

If an elephant didn't have a trunk, how would he smell?

Trunk or no trunk, he'd still smell terrible!

Linda Kay Rublesky, age 9
Willingbore, New Jersey

Illustrations by Quentin Blake

31

THE BUNK BED
ANDREW BRONIN

"I want the bottom bunk," said Gus.
"I want the bottom bunk, too,"
said Buster.
"We will flip for it," said Gus.
Gus took a shiny coin
from his pocket.
"Heads or tails?" he asked.
"Tails," said Buster.
Gus flipped the coin
high in the air and caught it.

Illustrations by Merle Peek

"Heads," said Gus. "You lose."
And he put the coin in his pocket.
"You didn't let me see it,"
said Buster.
"Don't you trust me?" asked Gus.
"If I were in the desert
and you had all the water,
I would trust you," said Buster.
"If I were climbing a mountain
and you were holding the rope,
I would trust you," said Buster.
"But when it comes to bunk beds,"
said Buster, "I do not trust you."

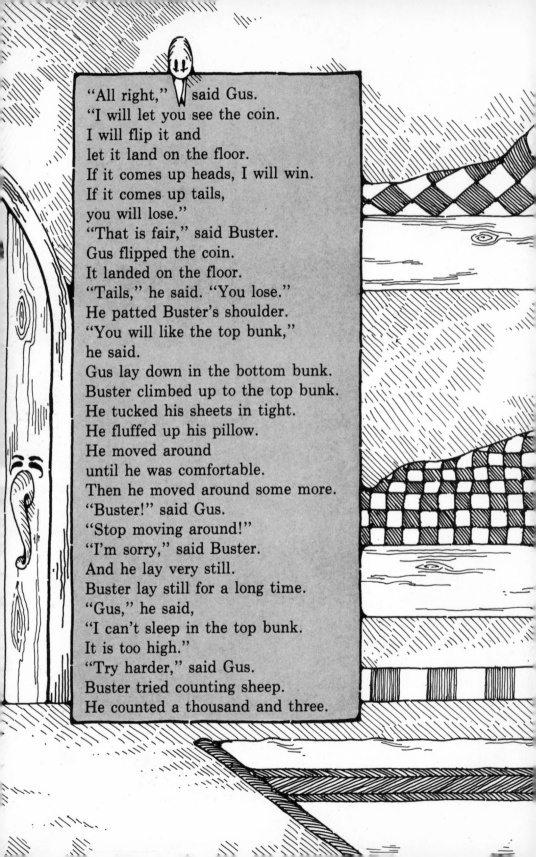

"All right," said Gus.
"I will let you see the coin.
I will flip it and
let it land on the floor.
If it comes up heads, I will win.
If it comes up tails,
you will lose."
"That is fair," said Buster.
Gus flipped the coin.
It landed on the floor.
"Tails," he said. "You lose."
He patted Buster's shoulder.
"You will like the top bunk,"
he said.
Gus lay down in the bottom bunk.
Buster climbed up to the top bunk.
He tucked his sheets in tight.
He fluffed up his pillow.
He moved around
until he was comfortable.
Then he moved around some more.
"Buster!" said Gus.
"Stop moving around!"
"I'm sorry," said Buster.
And he lay very still.
Buster lay still for a long time.
"Gus," he said,
"I can't sleep in the top bunk.
It is too high."
"Try harder," said Gus.
Buster tried counting sheep.
He counted a thousand and three.

He was still awake.
Buster tried to put himself
to sleep bit by bit.
"Go to sleep, toes," he whispered.
His toes fell asleep.
"Go to sleep, feet," he whispered.
His feet fell asleep.

"Go to sleep, legs," he whispered.
His legs fell asleep.
But by the time he got to his knees
his toes were wide awake again.
"Gus?" said Buster. "Are you awake?"
"How can I sleep when you
are whispering to your toes?"
said Gus.
Gus gnawed on his sheet.

"If I give you the bottom bunk,"
he said, "will you go to sleep?"
"Yes," said Buster. "I promise."
They switched bunks.
Buster crawled into Gus's warm bed.
"Thank you, Gus," he said.
"I am almost asleep already."
And in a moment, he was.
Gus lay in the top bunk,
and stared at the ceiling.

My Sister Laura
Spike Milligan

My sister Laura's bigger than me
And lifts me up quite easily.
I can't lift her—I've tried and tried;
She must have something heavy inside.

Illustration by Trina Schart Hyman

CLOCK

BY VALERIE WORTH

This clock
Has stopped,
Some gear
Or spring
Gone wrong—
Too tight,
Or cracked,
Or choked
With dust;
A year
Has passed
Since last
It said
Ting ting
Or tick
Or tock.
Poor
Clock.

ILLUSTRATED BY MERLE PEEK

Lucille Clifton
Everett Anderson's Year

Woodcuts by Ann Grifalconi

January

"Walk tall in the world,"
says Mama to Everett Anderson.
"The year is new and
so are the days—
walk tall in the world," she says.

February

Everett Anderson in the snow
is a specially
ice cream boy to know
as he jumps and calls
and spins and falls
with his chocolate nose and
vanilla toes.

March

What if a wind
would blow a boy away,
where would he ever go to play?
What if a wind
would blow him back next day,
what would his Mama say?
This time instead of run outside—
Everett Anderson thinks he'll hide.

41

April

Rain is good
for washing leaves
and stones and bricks and
even eyes,
and if you hold
your head just so
you can almost see
the tops of skies.

May

Remember the time we took a ride
to the country and saw a horse and a cow,
and remember the time I picked a weed
and Daddy laughed and laughed real loud,
and remember he spanked me for throwing a stone?
I wish it could be like that now—
thinks Everett Anderson when he's alone.

43

June

In 14A, till Mama comes home
bells are for ringing
and windows for singing
and halls are for skating
and doors are for waiting.

July

Everett Anderson thinks he'll make
America a birthday cake
only the sugar is almost gone
and payday's not till later on.

August

Now I am seven Mama can stay
from work and play with me all day.
I'll teach her marbles and rope and ball
and let her win sometimes, and all
our friends will be calling each other and saying,
"Everett's Mama and him are playing."

September

I already know where Africa is
and I already know how to
count to ten
and I went to school every day last year,
why do I have to go again?

October

Don't run when you see
this terrible monster
with a horrible nose and
awful eyes;
under those jaggedy
monstery teeth
is Everett Anderson
in disguise!

November

Thank you for the things we have,
thank you for Mama and turkey and fun,
thank you for Daddy wherever he is,
thank you for me, Everett Anderson.

December

The end of a thing
is never the end,
something is always
being born like
a year or a baby.

"I don't understand,"
Everett Anderson says.
"I don't understand where
the whole thing's at."

"It's just about Love,"
his Mama smiles.
"It's all about Love and
you know about that."

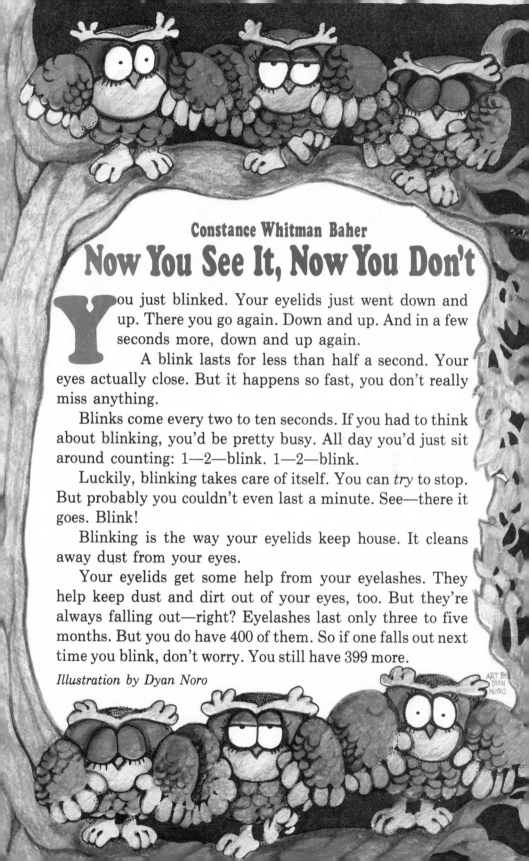

Constance Whitman Baher

Now You See It, Now You Don't

You just blinked. Your eyelids just went down and up. There you go again. Down and up. And in a few seconds more, down and up again.

A blink lasts for less than half a second. Your eyes actually close. But it happens so fast, you don't really miss anything.

Blinks come every two to ten seconds. If you had to think about blinking, you'd be pretty busy. All day you'd just sit around counting: 1—2—blink. 1—2—blink.

Luckily, blinking takes care of itself. You can *try* to stop. But probably you couldn't even last a minute. See—there it goes. Blink!

Blinking is the way your eyelids keep house. It cleans away dust from your eyes.

Your eyelids get some help from your eyelashes. They help keep dust and dirt out of your eyes, too. But they're always falling out—right? Eyelashes last only three to five months. But you do have 400 of them. So if one falls out next time you blink, don't worry. You still have 399 more.

Illustration by Dyan Noro

MEG'S EGG

Mary Ann Hoberman

Meg
Likes
A *reg*ular egg
Not a poached
Or a fried
But a *reg*ular egg
Not a devilled
Or coddled
Or scrambled
Or boiled
But an *egg*ular
*Meg*ular
*Reg*ular
Egg!

Illustration by Trina Schart Hyman

52

Serendipity

Eve Rice

Willie was wondering
if there might be a piece
of yesterday's cake left.
Polly walked by.
"Serendipity," Willie said.

"What's that?" asked Polly.
"A word. I like the sound
but I don't know what it means."
"Let's find out," Polly said.
Polly and Willie went
to the bookcase.

53

Illustrations by the author

"The dictionary is gone."
"Yes, but look," said Polly.
"Here is my skate key.
I have been looking for it."

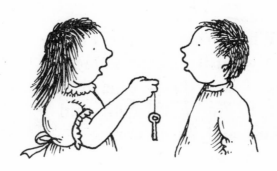

"It will not help us find what
serendipity means," said Willie.
"Come on."
Polly put the skate key
in her pocket.

They went to the desk.
There were many books
on the desk, and a shiny flute,
but the dictionary
was not there.

"Oh," said Polly,
"my bookmark!
I have been looking for it."
Just then the door slammed.
"Hello," called Mrs. Brimble.

Polly and Willie ran to the door.
"Do you know where
the dictionary is?" Willie asked.
"I think it is on the kitchen table."

Mrs. Brimble was right.
The dictionary was there.
Polly stopped by the sink.
"Here is my jar of blue paint.
I lost it this morning."

"Oh, you are always losing things,"
said Willie.
"But I find them again,"
Polly said.
"Let's find our word," said Willie.

They turned the pages
of the dictionary.
Finally they came to "serendipity."
Willie laughed.

"Let me see," said Polly.
She read aloud:
" 'Serendipity—being able to
discover good things by accident.'
Well, I discovered my skate key,
my bookmark, and my blue paint
today—all by accident."
"Yes," Willie said,
and we found a good word, too."

Mouse Dinner
Aileen Fisher

A mouse doesn't dine
on potatoes and beef . . .
he nibbles the seeds
from a pod or a sheaf.

He catches a beetle,
and then gives a brief
little wipe of his mouth
on a napkin of leaf.

59

Illustration by Cyndy Szekeres